She Is a
Baby Ghost

by Liza Charlesworth

ISBN: 978-1-338-78287-5
Illustrated by Diego Funck
Copyright © 2021 by Liza Charlesworth. All rights reserved.
Published by Scholastic Inc., 557 Broadway, New York, NY 10012

10 9 8 7 6 5 4 3 2 1   68   21 22 23 24 25 26 27/0

Printed in Jiaxing, China. First printing, June 2021.

She is a baby ghost.
She can crawl.

She is a baby ghost.
She can talk.

She is a baby ghost.
She can play.

She is a baby ghost.
She can eat.

She can throw, too.

She is a baby ghost.
She can sleep.

She is a baby ghost.
She can cry.

She is a baby ghost.
She can fly.

8